A PORCINE HISTORY OF PHILOSOPHY AND RELIGION

By
James Taylor

ABINGDON PRESS
Nashville · New York

A PORCINE HISTORY OF PHILOSOPHY AND RELIGION

Copyright © 1972 by Abingdon Press

ISBN 0-687-31745-2

MANUFACTURED BY THE PARTHENON PRESS AT
NASHVILLE, TENNESSEE, UNITED STATES OF AMERICA

To Janet and Peter
my farrow

PREFACE

It isn't clear to me why the idea for this little collection of cartoons didn't make itself known much earlier. I've always enjoyed drawing and I've always enjoyed theology, but somehow or other the two never got together until one day a year or so ago when one of my fellow teachers in a team-taught course was lecturing on some problem in axiology and I happened to have a scratch pad in front of me.

Why present philosophy and theology through pictures of pigs? Why indeed? One might as well ask why clutter up perfectly good cartooning with philosophy and theology. Actually the combination is quite natural. First, pigs are the wisest of all the farm animals, even as philosophers and theologians are (according to ancient tradition, at least, if not by modern evidence) the wisest of men. Second, theology is the most deeply enjoyable of all human endeavors (with philosophy—one would hope—not too poor a second); pigs have a greater capacity for enjoyment than any other animal; therefore it follows that there must be something theologian-like in every pig. We shall leave for another time the discussion of the validity of the corollary. Third, and most important, I find pigs easier to draw than most other animals.

A great deal of inspiration and quite a number of specific suggestions have been provided by the staff members of the course already mentioned—Mr.

Leo Werneke, Mr. William Landram, and Dr. Ann Marie Shannon. Other friends, notably the Reverend Douglas McPherson and his wife, Mary, made other suggestions and provided helpful criticism, as did my own patient wife, Helen. The best features of this collection are the result of what all these gracious and friendly people have contributed, and the book would no doubt have been a better one had I followed their advice more closely.

CONTENTS

I. CLASSIC GREEK PIGS

STOIC PIG

EPICUREAN PIG

SIMPLISTIC HEDONIST PIG ARISING ON A
MORNING AFTER TO SERVE AS AN OBJECT
LESSON TO MORE MODERATE PIGS EVERYWHERE

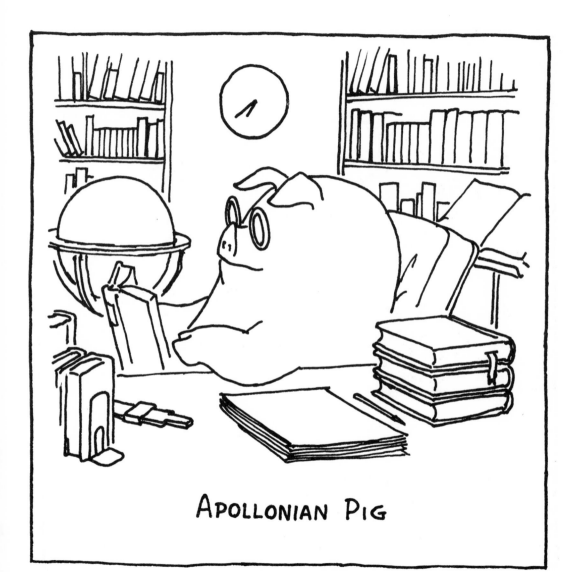

APOLLONIAN PIG

DIONYSIAN PIGS

A RECENT CONVERT TO THALES'
DOCTRINE, "ALL IS WATER."

A FOLLOWER OF DEMOCRITUS
IMMEDIATELY AFTER
CONSUMING A QUANTITY
OF PARTICULARLY
SMOOTH ATOMS

ANTI-HERACLITEAN PIG ATTEMPTING
TO STEP INTO THE SAME STREAM TWICE

SOCRATIC PIG AND DISCIPLE IN DIALOGUE

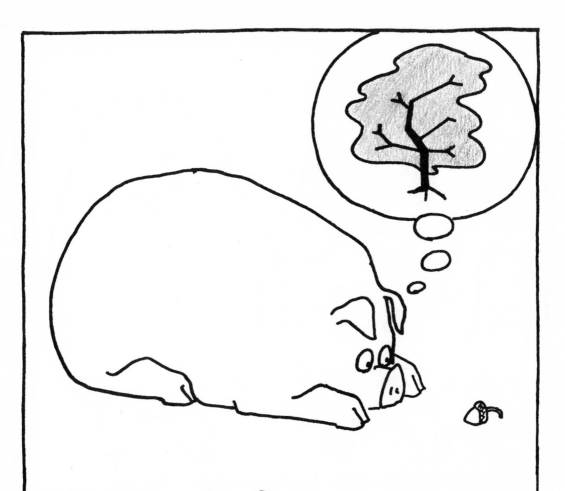

ARISTOTELIAN PIG CONTEMPLATING ACORN

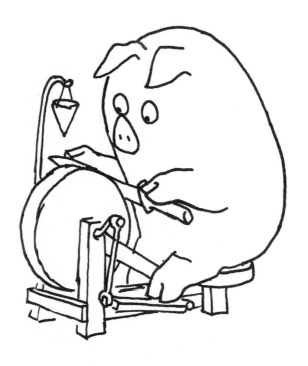

ARISTOTELIAN PIG PREPARING TO
DISTRIBUTE A MIDDLE TERM

II. PIGS OF THE ANCIENT
AND MEDIEVAL CHURCH

PELAGIAN PIG SINNING JUST
BECAUSE HE WANTS TO

BOETHIAN PIG BEING CONSOLED
BY PHILOSOPHY

REALIST PIG AND NOMINALIST PIG
CONTEMPLATING EAR OF CORN

OCKHAMIST PIG
PONDERING
MEANS OF
EXAMINING
PHILOSOPHICAL
ASSERTIONS

ABELARDIAN PIG RESOLVING
A YES AND NO QUESTION

FRANCISCAN PIG
AND CONGREGATION

III. PROTESTANT PIGS

ORTHODOX PRESBYTERIAN
PIG LOOKING FOR SIGNS OF
GRACE REVEALED

Anglican Pig Following the Via Media

ANGLICAN PIG GLORYING IN ONE OF THE
MORE PROVOCATIVE PASSAGES OF HOOKER'S
LAWS OF ECCLESIASTICAL POLITY

LITTLE BAND OF METHODIST PIGS
FLEEING FROM THE WRATH TO COME

METHODIST PIG WHOSE HEART
HAS BEEN STRANGELY WARMED

SOUTHERN BAPTIST PIG

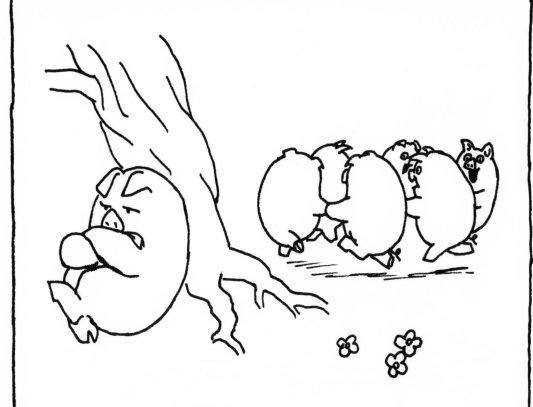

SOUTHERN BAPTIST PIG CAUGHT UP IN THE HEAT OF ECUMENICAL FERVOR

CAMPBELLITE PIG BEING SILENT
WHERE THE BIBLE IS SILENT

IV. MODERN PHILOSOPHICAL PIGS

PARTICULARLY NAÏVE
LEIBNIZIAN PIG DOING
RESEARCH ON MONADS

LEIBNIZIAN PIG PONDERING
THE DESIGN OF THE UNIVERSE

NOVICE CARTESIAN PIG TRYING
TO FIGURE OUT WHERE HE
MISSED THE POINT

BERKELEIAN PIG NOT BEING PERCEIVED

ROUSSEAUEAN PIG ENCOUNTERING
A NOBLE SAVAGE

HUMEAN PIG DEVELOPING A
CRITICISM OF THE ARGUMENT
FROM DESIGN

KANTIAN PIG PRIOR TO AWAKING
FROM HIS DOGMATIC SLUMBERS

KANTIAN PIG REFUSING TO LIE TO A
MANIAC WHO HAS ASKED THE
WHEREABOUTS OF HIS FRIEND

HEGELIAN PIG OBSERVING A THETICAL PIG
AND AN ANTITHETICAL PIG ARRIVING AT
A SYNTHESIS

KIERKEGAARDIAN
PIG TRYING
TO UNDERSTAND
ABRAHAM

KIERKEGAARDIAN PIG DEMONSTRATING
A LEAP OF FAITH

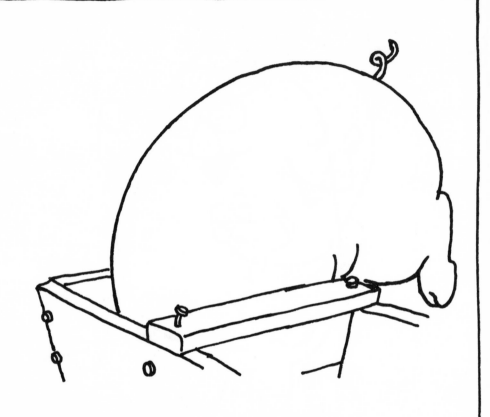

ENTHUSIASTIC CONVERT TO
FEUERBACH'S DOCTRINE,
"DER MENSCH IST WAS ER ISST".

V. TWENTIETH-CENTURY PIGS

NIETZSCHEAN SUPERPIG

A Follower of Rudolf Otto Experiencing the Mysterium Tremendum

A Liberal Pig Attempting to Practice
the Brotherhood of Pigs Under
the Fatherhood of God

LOGICAL POSITIVIST PIG DEVELOPING
AN INFORMAL LIST OF EMOTIVE TERMS

Two Sartrian Pigs in the
Days of the Resistance.

SITUATION ETHICS PIG AND PRINCIPLES
ETHICS PIG DISCUSSING THE NATURE
OF CHRISTIAN LOVE

MORALIST PIG PONDERING
A STRAIGHTFORWARD DECISION

MORALIST PIG PONDERING
AN AMBIGUOUS DECISION